Mark Twain

THE £ 1,000,000 BANK NOTE

Text adaptation, notes and activities
by Gina D. B. Clemen

Editor: Rebecca Raynes
Design: Nadia Maestri
Illustrations: Enzo Marciante
        coloured by Marina Tripodi

First edition: May 1997

5   4   3

Photogaphs taken from Cideb archive.

ISBN: 88-7754-356-6

Printed in Italy by Litoprint, Genoa

Contents

This story and the dossier sections are recorded in full on the cassette.

Introduction

A Note on Mark Twain

Mark Twain's real name was Samuel Langhorne Clemens. He was born in Florida, Missouri, U.S.A. in 1835. When he was a young boy he lived a happy life in Hannibal, Missouri, on the Mississippi River. In 1857 he worked as a pilot on a steamboat on the Mississippi. He liked travelling on this big river.

After the American Civil War started in 1861, Mark Twain went to California to look for gold. This was the time of the California Gold Rush.

In California, Twain's life changed. He began writing stories for a San Francisco newspaper, and he changed his real name, Samuel Clemens, to Mark Twain, a pen name.[1]

His short story, "The Celebrated Jumping Frog of Calaveras County," was a great success in 1865. Twain was now a famous writer. He travelled to Europe, The Holy Land and Hawaii. He wrote about his

---

1. **pen name** : a name used by a writer instead of his real name.

travels in *The Innocents Abroad* (1869) and *Roughing It* (1872).
Twain married Olivia "Livy" Langdon, a rich woman from New
England, and had three daughters. He lived in Hartford,
Connecticut with his family and wrote his three great books, *The
Adventures of Tom Sawyer* (1876), *Life on the Mississippi* (1883)
and *The Adventures of Huckleberry Finn* (1884). In these books he
remembered his youth on the Mississippi River. His other works
include *The Prince and the Pauper* (1880), *A Connecticut Yankee
in King Arthur's Court* (1889) and many short stories.

At the end of his life, Twain was a very sad man because he lost his
wife and two daughters. He died in 1910 at the age of seventy-five.
Mark Twain was the first American writer to change the American
way of writing, with his lively humour [1] and satire. [2]

---

1. **humour** : fun, amusement.
2. **satire** : writing that exposes and ridicules the faults of society.

SAN FRANCISCO IN THE 1850's

At the beginning of the 1800's, San Francisco, then called Yerba Buena, was a quiet Spanish village. There were a presidio, [1] a Spanish church, called Mission Dolores, and some simple homes. There were few ships in the big bay.

With the discovery of gold at Sutter's Fort, in 1848, everything changed. San Francisco suddenly grew into a busy city. In only one year, its population went from 1,000 to 30,000. Settlers came from all over the world. They came to open shops, saloons, hotels, restaurants, banks and trading companies. [2]

1. **presidio** : Spanish word for military fort.
2. **trading companies** : companies that buy and sell things.

There was a population explosion in California. The new settlers needed all types of things from the industries on the East Coast. The sea route from New York to San Francisco became an important one. The port of San Francisco was full of sailing ships.

In the 1850's, at the time of this story, San Francisco was the most important city on the Pacific Coast. The important gold mines in the Sierra Nevada Mountains had their offices in San Francisco. And that is where this story begins.

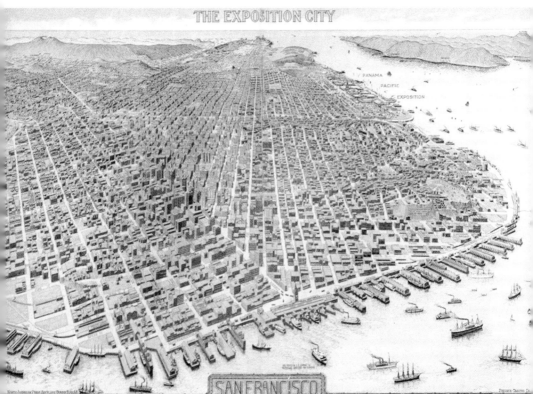

Are these sentences true (T) or false (F)?
Correct the false ones.

		T	F
a.	The old name of San Francisco was Yerba Buena.	☐	☐
b.	At the beginning of the 1800's, there were a lot of ships in the big bay.	☐	☐
c.	In only one month, its population went from 1,000 to 30,000.	☐	☐
d.	Settlers came from all over the world.	☐	☐
e.	In the 1850's, San Francisco was the most important city in America.	☐	☐
f.	This story begins in the Sierra Nevada Mountains.	☐	☐

....

....

....

THE £ 1,000,000
BANK NOTE

Before you read

Listen to Part 1 and put the pictures in the order they are mentioned.

a ☐

b ☐

c ☐

d ☐

e ☐

f ☐

1. From San Francisco to London

When I was 27 years old, I worked in an office in San Francisco. I did my job well and my future was promising. [1] I was alone in the world and I was happy.

On Saturday afternoons I didn't work. I sailed my little sailboat [2] on San Francisco Bay. One Saturday

---

1. **promising** : (here) favourable.

2. **sailboat** :

The £ 1,000,000 Bank Note

afternoon, I sailed out too far. The strong afternoon wind pushed my sailboat out of the bay, into the Pacific Ocean.

That night, when I had lost all hope, a small British brig [1] saw me and took me on board. The brig was sailing to London. The voyage was long and stormy. I worked as a sailor to pay for my trip.

When I arrived in London, my clothes were old and dirty. I had only one dollar in my pocket. With this dollar, I ate and slept for the first twenty-four hours. During the next twenty-four hours, I didn't eat and I didn't sleep.

At about ten o'clock, the following morning, I went to Portland Place. I saw a child walking past, holding a big pear. The child ate one small piece and then threw the pear onto the street.

I stopped and looked at it. I was very hungry and I really wanted

1. **brig** : sailing ship.

that pear. But every time I tried to get it, someone passed by and looked at me. I quickly turned in the other direction and waited for the person to pass by. I tried again and again to get that pear, but the same thing happened. I was desperate. I decided to get the pear and not to worry about the people who saw me. At that moment, a gentleman opened a window behind me and said, "Come in here, please."

A well-dressed servant [1] opened the door. He took me to a beautiful room. Here, two old gentlemen were sitting and discussing something important.

1. **servant** : person who works in a house.

The £ 1,000,000 Bank Note

Their breakfast was still on the table. I was very hungry and I stared [1] at their breakfast.

I want to tell the reader that the two gentlemen had made a bet [2] several days before. I knew nothing about the bet until later. Let me tell you what happened.

1. **stared** : looked at for a long time with wide-open eyes.
2. **bet** : agreement to risk money on the result of a future event in the hope to win more money.

1 What happened in Part 1?

a. Where does the story begin?

b. What did the strong wind do to the sailboat?

c. How did the narrator of the story reach London?

d. Why did the narrator want the pear?

e. What were the two old gentlemen doing?

2 Match the following words with their opposites.

future	unhappy
long	big
old	ugly
little	shut
happy	clean
dirty	short
open	past
beautiful	new

SAILING SHIPS

The first ships with sails were the Egyptian ships of the year 3000 BC. Egyptian ships had one square sail and one mast. [1] They sailed up and down the Nile River.

The Roman ships of the year 200 AD had one square sail, with a topsail [2] above it. In front of the ship there was a foresail. [3] The Roman ships had only one mast.

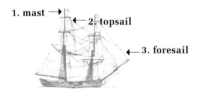

1. mast → 2. topsail
3. foresail

The Vikings from the north also had ships with one square sail and one mast.

The Egyptians, the Romans and the Vikings all used oars [1] to guide their ships.

The first sailing ships with two or more masts came from China. Marco Polo, the Italian merchant and traveller, brought this new idea from China to Italy in 1295.

Between the years 1400 and 1600, sailing ships changed a lot.

By the end of the 1400's, ships with three masts were common in Europe.

After the 1750's, European sailing ships had from two to six masts. Different types of ships had different names: the caravel, the carrack, the galleon, the schooner, the brig, the brigantine. These ships sailed all over the world.

1. **oars** :

The new clipper sailing ship was very fast and light. It sailed at great speed. In 1854 the clipper ship, *Flying Cloud*, travelled from New York to San Francisco in only 89 days and 8 hours. This was half the time of other ships.

During the California Gold Rush in the 1850's and 1860's, thousands of people travelled on clippers from New York to San Francisco. From San Francisco, these people went to the California Gold Country to look for gold.

The English brig, that took the narrator of the story to London, had two masts and two large, square sails.

Choose the correct answer:

a. The first ships with sails were the:

- [ ] Roman ships
- [ ] Egyptian ships
- [ ] caravels

b. To guide their sailing ships, the Egyptians and the Romans used:

- [ ] a square sail
- [ ] mast
- [ ] oars

c. The first sailing ships with two or more masts came from:

- [ ] Italy
- [ ] China
- [ ] Egypt

d. The fastest sailing ship was the:

- [ ] clipper
- [ ] brig
- [ ] brigantine

e. In the 1850's and 1860's, thousands of people travelled on clipper ships to reach:

- [ ] New York
- [ ] San Francisco
- [ ] London

f. The narrator of the story travelled to London on a:

- [ ] clipper
- [ ] schooner
- [ ] brig

SAILING ON SAN FRANCISCO BAY

Sailing on San Francisco Bay was popular in the 1800's and it still is today. There is always a lot of wind in San Francisco and this is perfect for sailing and windsurfing. The wind usually comes from the West and the North West. [1] The West wind is a strong wind, but it is not cold. When the wind is very strong, it can push small sailboats out of the bay and into the Pacific Ocean.

The waters of San Francisco Bay are cold all year. Their temperature in

1. **West and the North West :** ➜

24

the summer is between 10° and 13° C. Sharks [1] often swim in the bay. There are a lot of exciting regattas on the bay. When there is an important regatta, there are hundreds of sailboats with colourful sails.

In San Francisco, the sailing season begins the last Sunday of April, and finishes at the end of October.

1. **shark** :

Forty kilometres outside San Francisco Bay, in the Pacific Ocean, there are the Farallon Islands. Here, there is a Marine Sanctuary; a protected place where fish, whales, [1] seals [2] and rare birds live.

In winter and in spring, grey whales visit the Farallon Islands. In autumn, the huge [3] blue whale swims past these islands.

Outside San Francisco Bay, there is another Marine Sanctuary called Point Reyes Peninsula. Seals and rare birds live on this beautiful peninsula.

1. **whale** :

2. **seal** :

3. **huge** : enormous.

1 Match the correct parts of the sentences:

a. The wind usually comes
b. The West wind is strong
c. The waters of San Francisco Bay
d. The sailing season begins
e. The Farallon Islands are

f. Huge blue whales swim past

1. in autumn.
2. are cold all year.
3. in spring.
4. a Marine Sanctuary.
5. from the West and North West.
6. but not cold.

2 Can you find the hidden names of the four animals that live in the Farallon Island Marine Sanctuary?

R	W	P	O	S	G	F	E	I
S	Z	H	R	B	I	R	D	S
E	C	B	A	T	U	V	G	J
A	N	T	M	L	F	C	W	K
L	J	H	V	Q	E	N	F	M
S	T	D	C	F	I	S	H	Y
C	A	S	T	F	O	G	W	N

Before you read

Listen to the first four paragraphs of Part 2. Then choose the correct answer.

a. The two old gentlemen were:

☐ good friends
☐ brothers
☐ cousins

b. They decided to end their argument with:

☐ a strange promise
☐ a cup of tea
☐ a bet

c. The Bank of England issued two banknotes of:

☐ a million pounds each
☐ half a million pounds each
☐ eight million pounds each

d. The Bank of England issued the banknotes:

☐ to pay a debt with a foreign country
☐ for a private transaction
☐ for a public transaction with a foreign country

e. If a stranger arrived in London without money, except for the £ 1,000,000 banknote:

☐ he would spend it all
☐ he would starve to death
☐ he would be very happy

f. If he went to the bank to change the big note, the police would:

☐ help him find the owner of the note
☐ ask him many questions
☐ put him in prison

HARRIS'S
EATING PLACE

2. An Unusual Bet

The two old gentlemen were brothers. For several days, they argued [1] about a very strange subject. They decided to end their argument with a bet, as the English usually do. The following was the subject of the bet.

The Bank of England issued two banknotes of a million pounds each for a public transaction with a foreign country. England used one banknote and the other remained in the bank.

---

1. **argued** : discussed, debated.

The £ 1,000,000 Bank Note

At this point, Brother A said to Brother B, "If an honest and intelligent stranger arrives in London without a friend and without money, except for the £ 1,000,000 banknote, he will starve to death." [1]

Brother B answered, "No! I don't agree."

---

1. **starve to death** : die from lack of food.

An Unusual Bet

Brother A said, "If he goes to the bank or anywhere else to change this big note, the police will put him in prison. Everyone will think he stole [1] it."

They continued arguing for days, until Brother B said, "I'll bet £ 20,000 that the stranger will live for thirty days with the banknote and not go to prison."

Brother A accepted the bet. He went to the bank and bought the £ 1,000,000 banknote. After, he returned home and prepared a letter. Then the two brothers sat by the window and waited for the right man for the bet.

They saw a lot of honest faces go by, but they were not intelligent enough. Several faces were intelligent, but they were not honest. A lot of faces were honest and intelligent, but they were not poor enough. [2] Other faces were honest, intelligent and poor, but they were not strangers.

When they saw me from the window, they thought I was the right man. They asked me questions, and soon they knew my story. Finally, they told me I was the right man for the bet. I asked them to explain the bet. One of the gentlemen gave me an envelope.

---

1. **stole** : took what belongs to another person (to steal - stole - stolen).
2. **poor enough** : sufficiently poor.

The £ 1,000,000 Bank Note

I wanted to open it, but he said, "No, don't open it now. Wait until you are in your hotel room. Then read it very carefully."

I was confused and I wanted to discuss the subject with them. But they didn't. I felt hurt [1] because I was the subject of a joke. [2]

When I left their house, I looked for the pear on the street. It was gone. I was quite angry with those two gentlemen.

Far from their house, I opened the envelope. I saw that there was money inside! I didn't stop to read their letter.

1. **hurt** : (here) offended.
2. **subject of a joke** : made to look ridiculous.

An Unusual Bet

I ran to the nearest eating place. I ate and ate and ate. At last, I took out the envelope with the money, to pay for my meal. I looked at the banknote and almost fainted. [1] It was a banknote worth [2] five million dollars!

I was speechless. [3] I stared at the banknote. The two gentlemen had made a big mistake. They

probably wanted to give me a one-pound banknote.

I saw the owner of the eating place staring at the banknote, too. We were both surprised. I did not know what to do or say. So, I simply gave him the note and said, "Give me the change, please."

---

1. **fainted** : lost consciousness.
2. **worth** : with the value of.
3. **speechless** : not able to speak.

The £ 1,000,000 Bank Note

The owner apologized [1] a thousand times.

"I'm very sorry, but I can't change this banknote, sir."

"I don't have any other money. Please change this note."

The owner then said, "You can pay for this food whenever you want, sir. I understand that you are a very rich gentleman. You like playing jokes on people by dressing like a poor man. You can come here and eat all you want, whenever you want. You can pay me when you want."

1. **apologized** : said he was sorry.

1 **What happened in Part 2?**

a. What did Brother A say to Brother B? Did Brother B agree?

b. What was the subject of the bet?

c. How much money did Brother B bet?

d. Why was the narrator of the story the right man for the bet?

e. What was inside the envelope?

f. Why did the owner of the eating place apologize?

2 **The Past Simple is often used to write a story. Here's a crossword puzzle for you to do.**

What's the Past Simple of:

Across

1. say   **2.** argue   **3.** feel
4. are   **5.** steal   **6.** run
7. take

Down

8. make   **9.** do   **10.** give
11. leave   **12.** see   **13.** go
14. tell

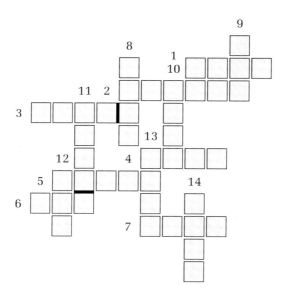

THE ENGLISH AND BETTING

Betting on things that will happen is common in Great Britain. The British love betting. They bet on horse races, dog races, football matches, cricket matches, hockey matches, polo matches and other sports. They also play the lottery.

A lot of betting is very informal. It takes place at the pub. The sum of money that is bet can be small, or very large, depending on the bet. The famous novel by Jules Verne, *Around the*

World in Eighty Days, is the story of an English gentleman who made a big bet. He bet that he could go around the world in eighty days, and then return to his club in London, at a specific time and day.

There are other forms of betting called gambling, where you play cards or other games for money.

In the United States, an entire city was built for people who like gambling. It's called Las Vegas. The city of Las Vegas, in the state of Nevada, has thousands of places where people can gamble small sums and big ones.

1 Are these sentences true (T) or false (F)? Correct the false ones.

	T	F
a. The British dislike betting on things.	☐	☐
b. They play the lottery.	☐	☐
c. It is not possible to bet at the pub.	☐	☐
d. *Around the World in Eighty Days* is the story of an important bet.	☐	☐
e. Playing cards for money is called gambling.	☐	☐
f. Las Vegas is a town in the state of California.	☐	☐

....

....

....

....

....

2 Discuss with your partner.

1. Are you a lucky person?

Yes ☐   No ☐

2. Do you bet on things?

Yes ☐   No ☐

If not, why not?

....

3. What do people bet on?

....

4. Describe an unusual bet you or somebody else made in the past.

....

Before you read

Listen to Part 3, and decide whether the sentences are true (T) or false (F). Then read the text, check your answers and correct the false ones.

		T	F
1.	The two gentlemen went to Egypt.	☐	☐
2.	They will return in a month.	☐	☐
3.	The family went to the Continent.	☐	☐
4.	There were two signatures on the letter.	☐	☐
5.	The two old gentlemen were playing a game.	☐	☐
6.	The narrator didn't know anything about the details of the bet.	☐	☐
7.	The narrator decided to keep the bill for a whole year.	☐	☐

3. The Letter

When I left the eating place, I hurried [1] to the house of the two gentlemen. I wanted to correct the mistake they had made. I was very nervous.

When I arrived, the same servant opened the door. I asked for the two gentlemen.

"They are gone," the servant said.

"Gone? Gone where?"

"Oh, on a journey."

---

1. **hurried** : went quickly.

The £ 1,000,000 Bank Note

But, where did they go?"

"To the Continent,[1] I think."

"The Continent?"

"Yes, sir."

"When will they return?"

"In a month."

"A month! Oh, this is awful![2] How can I talk to them? It's extremely important."

"I can't help you. I don't know where they are, sir."

"Then I must see a member of the family."

"All the family are away. They're in Egypt and India, I think."

"Before leaving, the two gentlemen made an enormous mistake. They will certainly return home tonight. Tell them that I came here to correct the mistake. I will return tomorrow."

"I'll tell them if I see them. But I won't see them!

1. **Continent** : mainland Europe.
2. **awful** : terrible.

The Letter

Sir, you must not worry because everything is all right. They will be here on time, and they will see you then. Good-bye."

I was confused. My head was in a fog. I did not understand what the servant told me. The letter — I remembered the letter! This is what it said:

> *You are an intelligent and honest man. You are also poor and a stranger. In this envelope you will find some money. It is yours only for 30 days. At the end of 30 days, return to this house. I have a bet on you. If I win this bet, you can have any job with any salary that you want.*

There were no signature, no address, no date on the letter.

How strange! I didn't know what to think. I went to a park, sat down and thought about what to do. After an hour, I reached the decision that follows.

The two old gentlemen are playing a game that I don't understand. They are betting on me. (But, at that time, I didn't know anything about the details of the bet.)

The £ 1,000,000 Bank Note

If I go to the Bank of England to return the banknote, the bank will ask me lots of questions. If I tell the truth, no one will believe me. They will put me in an asylum. [1] If I tell a lie, the police will put me in prison. I can't even give it to anyone, because no honest person will want it.

1. **asylum** : mental hospital.

The Letter

I can do only one thing: I must keep the bill [1] for a whole month. And, I must not lose it. If I help the old man to win his bet, he will give me the job I want.

The idea of an important job with a big salary made me happy. With this exciting idea in mind, I began walking down the streets of London.

1. **bill** : (here) banknote.

1 **What happened in Part 3?**

a. Why did the narrator hurry to the house of the two gentlemen?
b. Where did the two gentlemen go?
c. What did the letter say?
d. Why didn't the narrator return the banknote to the Bank of England?
e. What did the narrator plan to do?
f. Which idea made him happy?

2 **Match the correct parts of the sentences.**

a. The two gentlemen went   1. I'll go to prison.
b. The family went   2. there was some money.
c. My head was   3. were playing a game.
d. In the envelope   4. to the Continent.
e. The two gentlemen   5. they'll put me in an asylum.
f. If I tell a lie   6. in a fog.
g. If I tell the truth   7. to Egypt and India.

LONDINIUM

The Romans founded London almost 2000 years ago on the River Thames. [1] They named it Londinium, and it was part of the province called Britannia. The Romans always founded their colonies near a river. The Roman historian Tacitus wrote that Londinium was a busy centre for trade [2] and traders. The geographic position of Londinium, on the river and near the sea, was perfect for trade.

London was almost destroyed by the plague [3] in 1665, and by fire in 1666. In the 19th century, people began moving from the centre to the outer parts. [4]

Old Londinium is now the part of London called the City, a small area on

1. **Thames** : pronounced temʒ.
2. **trade** : buying, selling, exchanging things.
3. **plague** : an infectious, usually fatal disease.
4. **outer parts** : the edges of the city.

the north bank of the River Thames. The
City is the principal banking and
commercial centre of Europe. There are
more than 500 foreign banks and
hundreds of financial companies in this
area.

In the City there is still a part of an old
Roman wall, and the remains of
mediaeval London. The City has its own
cathedral, St. Paul's, and its own arts
centre, the Barbican. There is also an
excellent museum, the Museum of
London. This museum presents
London's history from Roman times.

1 How much do you know about London's history? Here's a crossword puzzle for you to do.

Across

1. Founders of London.
2. River of London.
3. Exchange of things.
4. Today's name for old Londinium.

Down

5. Roman historian.
6. Roman name for London.
7. Arts centre in the City.

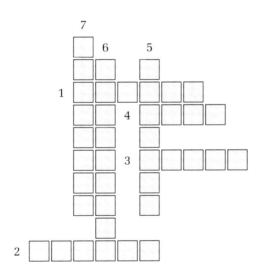

A map of the centre of London

1. Houses of Parliament
2. Westminster Abbey
4. Westminster Cathedral
8. National Gallery
12. National Film Theatre
13. National Theatre
15. Royal Opera House

2 Look at the map.
Can you find some of the places we've talked about in the City?

a. Which ones? ....

b. How many parks can you count on the map? ....

c. How many museums can you count? ....

d. How many theatres can you count? ....

e. What's the name of the lake in Hyde Park? ....

Before you read

Listen to the first four paragraphs of Part 4, and then choose the correct answer.

a. The narrator wanted:

- [ ] to use the £ 1,000,000 note
- [ ] to talk to the tailor
- [ ] to buy some new clothes

b. He passed in front of the tailor's:

- [ ] six times
- [ ] sixteen times
- [ ] sixty times

c. He quietly asked if they had:

- [ ] an elegant suit
- [ ] an old, unattractive suit
- [ ] new clothes

d. A man took him to:

- [ ] the back room
- [ ] the back of the shop
- [ ] a black room

e. When it was time to pay, the narrator:

- [ ] didn't have the £ 1,000,000 note
- [ ] didn't have any small change
- [ ] decided not to buy the suit

f. The narrator asked if he could pay:

- [ ] in a month
- [ ] in a week
- [ ] in a few days

4. At the Tailor's

Every time I passed in front of a tailor's, [1] I wanted to enter and buy some new clothes. But, I had no money to pay for them. The £ 1,000,000 banknote in my pocket was useless!

1. **tailor's** : shop that makes clothes for men.

At the Tailor's

I passed in front of the same tailor's six times. At last, I entered. I quietly asked if they had an old, unattractive suit that no one wanted to buy. The man I spoke to nodded [1] his head, but he didn't speak. Then another man looked at me and nodded his head. I went to him and he said, "One moment, please."

After some time, he took me to a back room. He looked at several ugly suits that no one wanted. He

1. **nodded** : moved his head up and down in agreement.

The £ 1,000,000 Bank Note

chose the worst for me. I really wanted a suit, so I said nothing.

It was time to pay. "Can you wait a few days for the money? I haven't got any small change [1] with me."

The man said, "Oh, you haven't? Well, I thought gentlemen like you carried large change."

"My friend," I replied, "you can't judge a stranger by the clothes he wears. I can pay for this suit. But, can you change a large banknote?"

"Oh, of course we can change a large banknote," he said coldly.

I gave him the banknote. He received it with a smile, a big smile that covered his face. When he read the banknote, his smile disappeared. The owner of the shop came over and asked me, "What's the trouble?" [2]

"There isn't any trouble. I'm waiting for my change."

"Come, come. Give him his change, Tod. Quickly!"

Tod answered, "It's easy to say, but look at the banknote."

1. **change** : (here) small banknotes, coins.
2. **trouble** : problem.

At the Tailor's

The owner looked at the banknote. Then he looked at my package with the ugly suit.

"Tod," he shouted, "you are stupid! How can you sell this unattractive suit to a millionaire! Tod, you can't see the difference between a millionaire and a poor man."

"I apologize, sir," the owner continued. "Please take off those things you are wearing and throw them in the fire. Put on this fine shirt and this handsome suit. It's perfect for you — simple but elegant."

I told him I was very happy with the new suit.

"Oh, wait until you see what we can make for you in your size! Tod, bring a pen and a book. Let me measure your leg, your arm..."

I didn't have a moment to speak.

The owner measured me.

The £ 1,000,000 Bank Note

Then he ordered his tailors to make me morning suits, evening suits, shirts, coats and other things.

"But, my dear sir," I said, "I can order all these things *only* if you change my banknote. Or, if you can wait a while [1] before I pay you."

"Wait *a while*! I'll wait *forever*, that's the word. Tod, send these things to the gentleman's address. Let the less important customers [2] wait!

What's your address, sir?"

1. **a while** : a period of time.
2. **customers** : clients, people who buy from a shop.

At the Tailor's

"I'm changing my home. I'll come back and give you my new address," I replied.

"Quite right, sir, quite right. Let me show you to the door, sir. Good day, sir, good day."

1 What happened in Part 4?

a. Why didn't the narrator buy new clothes?

b. What were the suits in the back room like?

c. What did the owner of the shop shout to Tod?

d. Why did the owner of the shop measure the narrator?

e. How long will the tailor wait before he is paid?

2 Complete the sentences with the phrases from the sign:

came over and asked
give you   in front of
come back   judge a stranger
between a millionaire
several ugly suits

1. Every time I passed .... a tailor's, I wanted to enter.

2. He looked at .... that no one wanted.

3. You can't .... by the clothes he wears.

4. The owner of the shop ...., "What's the trouble?"

5. Tod, you can't see the difference .... and a poor man.

6. I'll .... and .... my address.

HOW DID PEOPLE DRESS IN THE 1850's?

Clothes during this period were quite elegant. Men wore top hats, elaborate shirts, vests, [1] jackets and coats. Some wore big cloaks. [2] Women wore elaborate dresses, with long skirts. They also wore fashionable hats and bonnets, [3] and mantles. [4]

Women of the 1850's always wore gloves and carried a small umbrella, called a parasol. This parasol protected them from the sun.

1. **vest** :
2. **cloak** : long outer clothing without sleeves, shoulders or arms.
3. **bonnet** :
4. **mantle** : a short cloak.

Other examples of clothing in the 1850's.

Can you find seven hidden names of clothing worn in the 1850's? Look at the definitions of the words to help you.

- it protects you from the sun
- a piece of clothing without arms usually worn under a jacket
- a mantel worn over the shoulders
- you wear it on your head to give protection from the weather
- a hat worn by women with ribbons to tie under the chin.
- like a cloak
- you wear them on your hands

P	B	R	E	X	P	O	B	Y	O	U	C	Q
A	C	T	V	O	J	H	U	I	N	K	H	A
Q	O	S	I	E	A	M	A	N	T	L	E	L
X	Y	M	Q	A	S	C	K	O	G	H	W	P
S	P	A	G	D	B	T	H	D	M	F	Q	G
F	A	H	K	N	D	E	P	H	I	R	N	L
N	R	K	H	A	T	G	N	K	H	E	L	O
Z	A	J	O	D	A	Y	A	U	L	B	P	V
R	S	W	B	T	B	O	N	N	E	T	Y	E
C	O	S	T	B	L	U	E	A	N	C	B	S
B	L	C	N	C	H	V	R	J	R	K	O	X
S	P	F	W	A	I	D	Z	V	W	L	F	O

Before you read

Listen to the first four paragraphs of Part 5 and decide whether the sentences are true (T) or false (F). Then check your answers by reading the text and correct the false ones.

		T	F
1.	The narrator bought everything without money.	☐	☐
2.	Only one person was able to change the banknote.	☐	☐
3.	The narrator stayed at the Hancock Hotel.	☐	☐
4.	He always had dinner at the hotel.	☐	☐
5.	He preferred having lunch at Harris's simple eating place.	☐	☐
6.	Harris was happy with his new customers.	☐	☐
7.	The narrator lived like a rich, important man.	☐	☐

....
....
....
....
....
....
....
....

5. The Poor Millionaire

The impossible happened. I bought everything I wanted without money. I showed my banknote and asked for change, but every time the same thing happened. No one was able to change it.

I bought all that I needed and all the luxuries [1] that I wanted. I stayed at an expensive hotel in Hanover Square. I always had dinner at the hotel. But I preferred having breakfast at Harris's simple eating

1. **luxuries** : costly things that aren't necessary.

The £ 1,000,000 Bank Note

place. Harris's was the first place where I had a good meal with my million-pound note. That's where it all started.

The news about me and my banknote was all over London. Harris's eating place became famous because I had breakfast there. Harris was happy with all his new customers.

I lived like a rich, important man. I had money to spend. I lived in a dream. But often, I said to myself, "Remember, this dream will end when the two men return to London. Everything will change."

My story was in the newspapers. Everyone talked about the "strange millionaire with the million-pound note in his pocket." *Punch* magazine drew a funny picture of me on the front page. People talked about everything I did and about everything I said. They followed me in the streets.

I kept my old clothes, and sometimes I wore them. It was fun when the shop owners thought I was poor. Then I showed them the banknote, and, oh, how their faces changed!

After ten days in London, I went to visit the American ambassador. He was very happy to meet me. He invited me to a dinner-party that evening. He told me that he knew my father from Yale University. He

The Poor Millionaire

invited me to visit his home whenever I wanted.

I was glad to have a new, important friend.
I thought to myself, "I'll need an important friend,
when the story of the million-pound note and bet
comes out."

I want the reader to know that I planned to pay
back all the shop owners who sold me things on
credit. "If I win the bet for the old gentleman,"
I thought, "I will have an important job. With an
important job, I will have a big salary." I planned to
pay back everyone with my first year's salary.

1 **What happened in Part 5?**

a. Why did the narrator buy everything without money?

b. Where did he have breakfast and why?

c. What did *Punch* magazine do?

d. Why did the narrator keep his old clothes?

e. Who invited him to a dinner party?

f. What will he have if he wins the bet for the old gentleman?

2 **Put the jumbled letters in order and form a word. Then match the word to its meaning.**

a. esixluru

....

1. famous American university

b. neievxpse

....

2. what you wear

c. nyfun

....

3. first meal of the day

d. hsecotl

....

4. costly things that aren't necessary

e. afbkserat

....

5. costs a lot of money

f. lyea

....

6. makes you laugh

3 **Tick (✔) the words that refer to Harris's eating place.**

☐ clean   ☐ simple

☐ famous   ☐ good meal

☐ noisy   ☐ dirty

☐ serves breakfast   ☐ had new customers

MONEY AND ITS ORIGINS

Long ago there was no money. Banknotes and coins didn't exist. People used all kinds of things as money: food, salt, shells, [1] jewellery, precious metals, cloth, animals. They traded these things for something else. This kind of trading is called barter. Some primitive people still use the barter system. One of the greatest barters in history is the following: In 1626, Peter Minuit, of the Dutch West India Company, bought Manhattan Island (New York) from the Indians. He paid for it with beads and trinkets [2] worth $ 24! As time went on, people began to use coins made of gold, silver, copper [3] and other metals. Each country had its own coins of different sizes and shapes.

1. **shells** :
2. **beads and trinkets** :
3. **copper** : a soft, red metal.

Until the 1920's, banknotes were backed [1] by gold. This was called the "gold standard". It meant that when a person went to the bank and presented a banknote, the bank gave the person the same amount in gold. This is why the words "promise to pay" appeared on banknotes.

Today, coins and banknotes are made in a place called a mint. Banknotes are made with very special paper. This makes it extremely difficult for counterfeiters, people who print their own money, to copy the banknotes. It is against the law, in all countries, to counterfeit money.

Each country has its own currency [2] with its own name. When you go to a foreign country, you must change your currency with that of the country you are visiting. For example, the United States of America have the U.S. Dollar, Great Britain has the Pound, France has the Franc, Germany has the Mark and Japan has the Yen.

1. **backed** : (here) guaranteed.
2. **currency** : money.

66

1 Are these sentences true (T) or false (F)? Correct the false ones.

		T	F
1.	Long ago people used only jewellery and precious metals as money.	☐	☐
2.	Trading one thing for something else is called barter.	☐	☐
3.	Peter Minuit bought Manhattan Island (New York) from the Indians for $ 24 worth of beads and trinkets.	☐	☐
4.	The "gold standard" meant that only gold coins were used in a country.	☐	☐
5.	A mint is a place where banknotes are kept.	☐	☐
6.	Counterfeiters are people who print their own money.	☐	☐
7.	The currency of Germany is called the Franc.	☐	☐

....

....

....

....

....

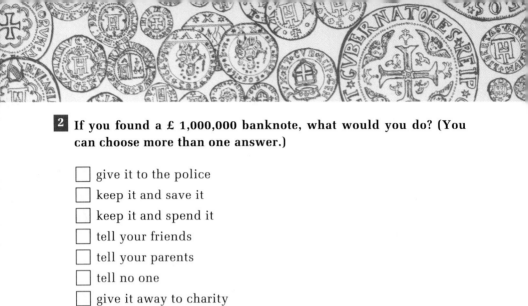

2 **If you found a £ 1,000,000 banknote, what would you do? (You can choose more than one answer.)**

☐ give it to the police
☐ keep it and save it
☐ keep it and spend it
☐ tell your friends
☐ tell your parents
☐ tell no one
☐ give it away to charity

3 **After finding the £ 1,000,000 banknote, and deciding what to do with it, how would you feel?**

☐ nervous
☐ happy
☐ worried
☐ excited
☐ unhappy
☐ guilty
☐ honest

4 **If you decided to keep it and spend it, what is the first thing you would buy?**

....
....
....

Crack [1] the code!

5 Can you crack the secret code and find the correct vowels for these words? When you crack the code, remember to write the correct vowels in the apple, and write the decoded words.

m✳n✤y   ....

b❋rt✤r   ....

g✳ld   ....

s❖lv✤r   ....

c✳pp✤r   ....

m✤t❋ls   ....

m❖nt   ....

c✳✯nt✤rf✤❖t   ....

c✯rr✤ncy   ....

b❋nkn✳t✤   ....

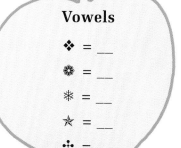

Vowels

❖ = ___

❋ = ___

✳ = ___

✯ = ___

✤ = ___

1. **crack** : break.

69

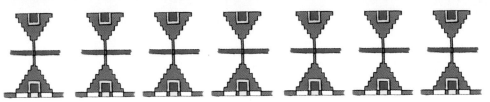

MONEY FROM OTHER TIMES AND OTHER PLACES

Old Roman Coins

Mexican   **French**

Republic of San Marino

German

Swiss   **Polish**   **Belgian**

Spanish   **Slovenian**

How are these coins similar?

....

How are they different?

....

Before you read

Listen to the first two pages of Part 6, and then choose the names of the person who said these words.

1. "I think I know you."
   - [ ] the American Ambassador
   - [ ] Lloyd Hastings
   - [ ] Portia Langham

2. "Yes, I'm the strange millionaire with the million-pound note in his pocket!"
   - [ ] the narrator
   - [ ] the Duke of Shoreditch
   - [ ] Lloyd Hastings

3. "Well, well, this *is* a surprise."
   - [ ] Lloyd Hastings
   - [ ] Henry Adams
   - [ ] the American Ambassador

4. "You had a very small salary."
   - [ ] Henry Adams
   - [ ] Portia Langham
   - [ ] Lloyd Hastings

5. "No, no, it was the What Cheer Restaurant."
   - [ ] Lloyd Hastings
   - [ ] Henry Adams
   - [ ] Viscount Cheapside

6. "That night we worked for six long hours on the Gould and Curry Mining Company papers."
   - [ ] the American Ambassador
   - [ ] Lloyd Hastings
   - [ ] Henry Adams

6. The Dinner Party

There were fourteen people at the dinner party. The Duke and Duchess of Shoreditch, and their daughter, Lady Anne-Grace-Eleanor de Bohun, the Earl and Countess of Newgate, Viscount Cheapside, Lord and Lady Blatherskite, the Ambassador and his wife and daughter, and some other people. There was also a beautiful, twenty-two-year old English girl, named Portia Langham. I fell in love [1] with her in two

---

1. **fell in love** : developed a great love for.

73

The £ 1,000,000 Bank Note

minutes, and she with me!

After a while, the house servant presented another guest, Mr. Lloyd Hastings. When Mr. Hastings saw me, he said, "I think I know you."

"Yes, you probably do."

"Are you the — the — "

"Yes, I'm the strange millionaire with the million-pound note in his pocket!"

"Well, well, this *is* a surprise. I never thought you were the same Henry Adams from San Francisco! Six months ago, you were working in the offices of Blake Hopkins in San Francisco. I remember clearly. You had a very small salary. And, at night, you helped me arrange the papers for the Gould and Curry Mining Company. Now you're a millionaire, a celebrity here in London. I can't believe it! How exciting!"

"I can't believe it, either, Lloyd."

"Just three months ago, we went to the Miner's Restaurant — "

"No, no, it was the What Cheer Restaurant."

"Right, it *was* the What Cheer. We went there at two o'clock in the morning. We had steak and coffee. That night we worked for six long hours on the Gould and Curry Mining Company papers. Do you remember, Henry, I asked you to come to London with me.

The Dinner Party

I wanted you to help me sell the Gould and Curry gold mine shares. [1] But you refused."

"Of course I remember. I didn't want to leave my job in San Francisco. And, I still think it's difficult to sell shares of a California gold mine here in London."

"You were right, Henry. You were so right. It is impossible to sell these shares here in London. My plan failed and I spent all my money. I don't want to talk about it."

"But you must talk about it. When we leave the dinner party, you must tell me what happened."

"Oh, can I? I really need to talk to a friend," Lloyd said, with water in his eyes.

"Yes, I want to hear the whole story, every word of it."

"Thank you, Henry. You're a true friend."

---

1. **shares** : documents you buy that make you part-owner of a business; investment in a business.

The £ 1,000,000 Bank Note

At this point, it was time for dinner. Thanks to the English system of precedence, [1] there was no dinner.

The Duke of Shoreditch wanted to sit at the head of the table. The American ambassador also wanted to sit at the head of the table. It was impossible for them to decide, so we had no dinner.

The English know about the system of precedence.

---

1. **precedence** : order to be observed in ceremonies by people of different rank.

The Dinner Party

They have dinner before going out to dinner. But strangers know nothing about it. They remain hungry all evening. Instead, we had a dish of sardines and a strawberry. Now it was time for everyone to play a game called cribbage. [1] The English never play a game for fun. They play to win or to lose something.

Miss Langham and I played the game, but with little interest. I looked at her beautiful face and said, "Miss Langham, I love you!"

1. **cribbage** : card game.

The £ 1,000,000 Bank Note

"Mr. Adams," she said softly and smiled, "I love you too!"

This was a wonderful evening. Miss Langham and I were very happy. We smiled, laughed and talked.

I was honest with her. I told her that I was poor and that I didn't have a cent in the world. I explained that the million-pound note was not mine. She was very curious to know more. I told her the whole story from the start. She laughed and laughed. She thought the story was very funny. I didn't understand why it was funny. I also explained that I needed an important job with a big salary to pay all my debts. [1]

"Portia, dear, can you come with me on the day I must meet those two gentlemen?

"Well, yes, if I can help you," she replied.

"Of course you can help me. You are so lovely that when the two gentlemen see you, I can ask for any job and any salary. With you there, my sweet Portia, the two gentlemen won't refuse me anything."

---

1. **debts** : money that must be paid back.

1 What happened in Part 6?

a. Where was the dinner party?

b. Describe Portia Langham.

c. Where did Lloyd Hastings first meet Henry Adams?

d. Why did Lloyd Hastings go to London?

e. Why was there no dinner?

f. What did Henry Adams tell Portia Langham?

2 Tick the correct answer.

a. Lloyd Hastings worked for:
   ☐ the American ambassador
   ☐ Gould and Curry Mining Company
   ☐ Blake Hopkins

b. In San Francisco, Henry and Lloyd had dinner at:
   ☐ the What Cheer Restaurant
   ☐ Harris's
   ☐ the Miner's Restaurant

c. Lloyd Hastings came to London to sell:
   ☐ a Nevada gold mine
   ☐ gold
   ☐ shares of a California gold mine

d. There was no dinner at the dinner party, but everyone:
   ☐ danced
   ☐ listened to music
   ☐ had a dish of sardines

e. Portia thought Henry's story was:
   ☐ funny
   ☐ curious
   ☐ interesting

LONDON TODAY

London today covers 100 square miles, with a population of about 7,000,000 people. It is one of Europe's most interesting capitals. The nation's government is the Parliament, at Westminster. In the clock tower near the House of Commons, is London's famous time-keeper, [1] Big Ben.

Magnificent Westminster Abbey is nearby. It was built in the 11th century by King Edward the Confessor. Many of England's kings and queens were crowned here.

Buckingham Palace is the Queen's impressive London home. In front of the Palace, visitors can enjoy the ceremony of the Changing of the Guard. It takes place at 11:30 a.m. daily in the summer, and on alternate days in the winter.

1. **time-keeper** : (here) clock.

Trafalgar Square, with Nelson's Column, is a busy place. The National Gallery is at Trafalgar Square. It has one of the best collections of European paintings from the 13th century to the 1900's.

Going east along the River Thames, there is the famous Tower of London and the 19th century Tower Bridge. The White Tower is the oldest part of the Tower of London. It was built by William the Conqueror in 1078. The Crown Jewels are kept in the Jewel House.

There are several beautiful parks to visit in London: Hyde Park, Kensington Gardens, St. James's Park, Battersea Park and Regent's Park with its zoo.

The area from Kensington Gardens to Cromwell Road is "museumland". The Science Museum, Natural History Museum,

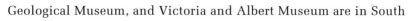

Geological Museum, and Victoria and Albert Museum are in South Kensington. The British Museum, one of the greatest museums of the world, is in the district of Bloomsbury.

London is a wonderful place to shop. The variety of things to buy is huge. In the West End, London's most fashionable shopping streets are Oxford Street, Regent Street and Bond Street. There are a lot of fine shops and department stores in the area of Piccadilly Circus.

Kensington High Street and King's Road are good shopping areas for young fashions.

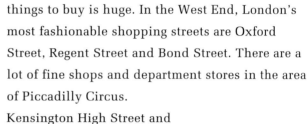

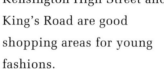

Knightsbridge is the home of Harrods, London's most famous department store.

Covent Garden is near Charing Cross. It was once a fruit and vegetable market. Now it is a covered shopping area, with elegant restaurants, bars, shops and street entertainers.

London has an excellent underground public transportation system, called the tube.

It takes people to all parts of London rapidly.

Can your find your way around London? Try this crossword puzzle.

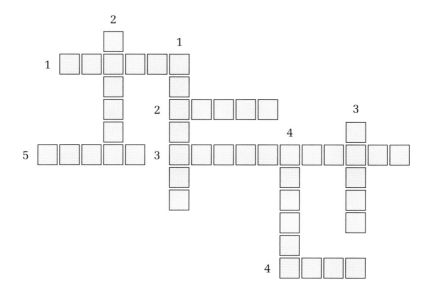

Across

1. London's River
2. Green areas in London
3. Runs under London
4. Place where you buy things
5. Tall, thin building

Down

1. Cathedral in the City
2. Buckingham ....
3. The King's wife
4. Men who protect the palace

Before you read

 1 **Listen to the first three paragraphs of Part 7, then choose the correct words in the sentences.**

1. At the *and/end* of the dinner *party/part*, I returned to the *house/hotel* with Hastings.
2. *She/He* talked about his *problems/projects*.
3. I was thinking about *Portland Place/Portia* the *hole/whole* time.
4. When *he/we* arrived at the *hostel/hotel*, Hastings said, "Let me just *stand/stay* here and look at this *magnificent/marvellous* hotel.
5. What *expensive/extensive* furniture!
6. You have *anything/everything* you *want/wish*.
7. This was my *latest/last* hope.

Now read the three paragraphs and check your answers.

86

2 **Now listen to the end of Part 7 and tick the correct answer.**

a. Lloyd sat down and drank:

☐ hot tea
☐ hot whisky
☐ hot milk

b. Lloyd didn't hear Hasting's story because:

☐ he was ill
☐ he was thinking about Portia
☐ he drank too much at the dinner party

c. Lloyd wanted to sell shares for:

☐ one million dollars
☐ three million dollars
☐ one million pounds

d. Any money Lloyd received over one million dollars:

☐ was for the owners of the company
☐ was for the Blake Hopkins Company
☐ was his to keep

e. Lloyd asked Henry to:

☐ work for the Gould and Curry Gold Mine
☐ return to San Francisco with him
☐ be the new owner of the mine

f. Henry will help Lloyd sell the shares:

☐ by using his money
☐ by using his name
☐ by using his banknote

7. A Million-Dollar Idea

At the end of the dinner party, I returned to the hotel with Hastings. He talked about his problems, but I didn't listen to him. I was thinking about Portia the whole time.

When we arrived at the hotel, Hastings said, "Let me just stand here and look at this marvellous hotel. It's a palace! What expensive furniture! You have everything you want. You are rich, Henry. And I am poor."

His words scared me. I, too, was poor. I didn't have a cent in the world, and I had debts to pay. I needed to win the gentleman's bet. This was my last hope. Hastings didn't know the truth.

"Henry, just a tiny part of your income can save me. I'm desperate!" Hastings cried.

"My dear Hastings, sit down here and drink this hot whisky. Now tell me your whole story, every word of it."

The £ 1,000,000 Bank Note

"Do you want to hear my story again?"

"But, you never told me your story."

"Of course I told you my story, as we walked to the hotel. Don't you remember?"

"I didn't hear one word of it."

"Henry, are you ill? Is something wrong with you? What did you drink at the dinner party?"

Oh, Hastings, I'm in love! I can only think about my sweet Portia. This is why I didn't hear your story before."

Hastings got up from his chair, shook my hand [1] and laughed.

"I'm very happy for you, Henry, very happy," he said smiling. "I'll tell you the whole story again."

So he sat down and patiently started to tell me his story.

To make a long story short, [2] the owners of the Gould and Curry Gold Mine

---

1. **shook my hand** :

2. **to make a long story short** : briefly, in short.

A Million-Dollar Idea

sent Henry to England, to sell the shares of the mine for one million dollars. Any money he received over one million dollars was his to keep. Hastings's dream was to sell the shares for more than one million dollars, and become rich. He had only one month to sell the shares. He had done everything to sell them, but nobody wanted to buy them.

Then he jumped up and cried, "Henry, you can help me! Will you do it?"

"Tell me how."

"Give me a million dollars and I'll sell you all the shares. You will be the new owner of the gold mine. Don't, don't refuse."

I did not know what to say. I wanted to tell Hastings the truth. But then, an intelligent idea came to me. I thought about it for a moment and then calmly said, "I will save you, Lloyd."

"Then I am already saved! How can I thank you — "

"Let me finish, Lloyd. I will save you, but not in that way. I have a better way. I know everything about that mine. I know its great value. You will sell the shares by *using my name*. You can send anyone to me, since people in London know me. I will guarantee the gold mine. In a week or two, you will sell the shares for three million dollars, by using my name. And we'll

The £ 1,000,000 Bank Note

share [1] the money you earn. Half to you and half to me."

Lloyd was very happy and excited. He danced around the room and laughed.

"I can use your name! Your name — think of it. The rich Londoners will run to buy these shares. I'm saved! And I'll never forget you, Henry!"

1. **share** : divide.

1 What happened in Part 7?

a. Why didn't Henry listen to Lloyd's problems?

b. Where did Henry and Lloyd go after the dinner party?

c. What was Lloyd's dream?

d. How did Lloyd ask Henry to help him?

e. How will Henry help Lloyd to sell the shares?

2 What do you know about the people in the story? Match the characters with the information below. Put the letters a-h in the correct boxes.

a. Henry Adams   1. ☐ works in a tailor's shop

b. Two old gentlemen   2. ☐ English nobleman

c. Harris   3. ☐ worked for Blake Hopkins

d. Tod   4. ☐ represents the United States of America in England

e. American Ambassador   5. ☐ made an unusual bet

f. Duke of Shoreditch   6. ☐ lovely, young English girl

g. Lloyd Hastings   7. ☐ owns an eating place

h. Portia Langham   8. ☐ wants to sell shares

3 How many words of 3 or more letters can you make from this title:

THE MILLION-POUND BANKNOTE

(three are already done for you)

lion	....	....
not	....	....
ate	....	....
....	....	....
....	....	....

Money in the United States and in Great Britain

American Money

The American monetary system is based on the dollar. The dollar is divided into 100 cents. Here are reproductions of the dollar bill, and coins with the heads of famous Americans.

British Money

The British monetary system is based on the pound sterling. The pound is divided into 100 pence.

There are four cupro-nickel coins:

£ $ £ $ £ $

There are two bronze coins:

The Queen's head appears on the front side of the coins, as you can see here. Notice that the 20 pence and the 50 pence have seven sides.

There is a pound coin:

There are four other bank notes:

Some people collect old and new coins and banknotes. This is their hobby.

Do you collect things? ....

What other things do people collect? ....

8. Back to Portland Place

The next day, all of London talked about the shares of the California gold mine. I stayed in my hotel and said to everyone who came to me, "Yes, I know Mr. Hastings. He's a very honest man. And I know the gold mine, because I lived in the California Gold Country. It is a mine of great value." People were now interested in buying the shares.

I spent every evening with Portia at the American Ambassador's house. I didn't tell her about the shares and the mine. It was a surprise. We talked about our

The £ 1,000,000 Bank Note

love and our future together.

Finally, the end of the month arrived. Lots of rich Londoners bought the shares of the mine. I had a million dollars of my own in the London and County Bank. And, Lloyd did too.

It was time to meet with the two old gentlemen. I dressed in my best clothes, and I went to get Portia.

Before going to Portland Place, Portia and I talked about the job and the salary.

Back to Portland Place

"Portia, you are so beautiful! When the two gentlemen meet you, they will give me any job and any salary I ask for."

"Henry, please remember that if we ask for too much, we will get nothing.

The £ 1,000,000 Bank Note

Then what will happen to us?"

"Don't be afraid, Portia."

When we arrived, the same servant opened the door. There were the two old gentlemen having tea. They were surprised to see Portia. I introduced her to them.

Then I said, "Gentlemen, I am ready to report [1] to you."

"We are pleased to hear this," said one gentleman. "Now we can decide the bet that my brother Abel and I made. If you won for me, you can have any job in my power. Do you have the million-pound note?"

"Here it is, sir," and I gave it to him.

"I won!" he shouted. "Now what do you say, Abel?"

"I say he survived, and I lost twenty thousand pounds. I can't believe it!"

"I have more to tell you," I said. "But, it's a long story. I'll tell you another time. For now, look at this."

"What! A Certificate of Deposit for £ 200,000. Is it yours?"

"It's mine. I earned it by using the banknote you lent me for a month."

---

1. **report** : (here) tell.

Back to Portland Place

"This is astonishing! I can't believe it."

Portia looked at me with surprise and said, "Henry, is that really your money? You didn't tell me the truth."

"No, I didn't. But, I know you'll forgive [1] me."

"Don't be so sure! You told me a lie, Henry."

"Dearest Portia, it was only for fun. Come, let's go now."

"But, wait, wait!" my gentleman said. "I want to give you the job

---

1. **forgive** : pardon, say that you are no longer angry with someone.

The £ 1,000,000 Bank Note

and the salary you choose."

"Thank you, thank you with all my heart. But I don't want the job."

"Henry, you didn't thank the good gentleman in the right way. Can I do it for you?" Portia said.

"Of course you can, my dear."

Portia walked to my gentleman, sat on his lap [1] and kissed him on the mouth.

Then the two old gentlemen shouted and laughed. I was amazed. What was happening?

"Papa," said Portia, "Henry doesn't want your job. I feel very hurt."

"Darling, is that your father?" I asked.

"Yes, he's my stepfather, [2] a dear man. Now do you understand why I laughed when you told me your story?"

"My dearest sir," I said, "I want to take back [3] what I said. There *is* a job that I want."

"Tell me!"

"I want the job of son-in-law." [4]

---

1. **lap** : (here) knees.
2. **stepfather** : the husband of Portia's mother, not her real father.
3. **take back** : change what I said before.
4. **son-in-law** : husband of the daughter.

Back to Portland Place

"Well, well, well. But you were never a son-in-law before. Do you know how to do this job?"

"Try me, please! Try me for thirty or forty years, and if — "

"Oh, all right. Take her!"

Were Portia and I happy? There aren't enough words in the dictionary to describe our happiness. When the Londoners heard the whole story of my adventures with the banknote, they talked of nothing else.

Portia's father took the banknote back to the Bank of England and cashed [1] it. Then he gave us the cancelled banknote as a wedding present. We put it in a picture frame [2] and hung it on the wall in our new home.

And so I always say, "Yes, it's a million-pound banknote, but it only bought one thing in its life: the most valuable thing in the world — Portia!"

---

1. **cashed** : changed into real money.

2. **picture frame** :

1 What happened in Part 8?

a. What did Henry tell the people who were interested in the gold mine?

b. How much money did Henry and Lloyd make by selling the shares?

c. Who lost the bet and how much did he lose?

d. Why was Henry amazed?

e. What job did Henry finally want?

f. Where did Henry and Portia put the million-pound banknote?

2 Can you make a summary of the story? Put these sentences in the correct order. Write 1, 2, 3 etc. in the boxes. Three are done for you.

a ☐ I agreed to help Lloyd to sell the shares, by using my name.

b ☐ When I returned to the two gentlemen's house, they had gone to the Continent.

c ☐ The two gentlemen gave me an envelope with money and a letter inside.

d ☐ At the end of the month, I returned to the two gentlemen's house and showed them the million-pound note.

e ☐ The owner of the eating place apologized because he was not able to change the banknote.

f ☐ Lloyd asked me to help him sell the shares of a California Gold Mine.

g ☐ When I arrived in London, I had only one dollar in my pocket.

h ☐ The owner of the tailor's ordered his tailors to make me suits, shirts and coats.

i ☐ When I opened the envelope and saw the million-pound banknote, I almost fainted.

j ☐ I had won the bet for the old gentleman, and I asked him for the job of son-in-law.

k 3 At Portland Place, two gentlemen made a bet, and I was the right man for the bet.

l 1 One Saturday afternoon I sailed out too far, and the strong wind blew my sailboat into the Pacific Ocean.

m 7 He thought I was a rich gentleman who liked playing jokes on people by dressing like a poor man.

n ☐ At a dinner party, I met Portia Langham and Lloyd Hastings.

o ☐ Lots of rich Londoners bought the shares of the gold mine, and Lloyd and I became rich.

3 What other English words about money do you know? Make a spidergram like this:

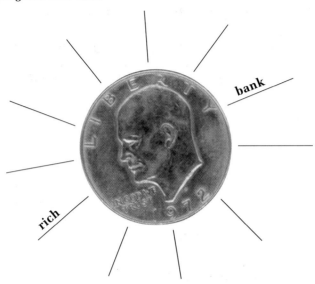

bank

rich

4 Write a "book report" of this story.

Title ....

Author ....

Characters   main ....

                           minor ....

Setting   place(s) ....

                           time ....

Short summary

This book is about ....

....

....

5 A journalist from *Punch* magazine interviews Henry Adams. Read this interview with Henry Adams, and then, with a partner, fill in the blank spaces using the words from the box.

> horse bought rode countryside everything strange
> follow British twenty-seven weeks humour people
> famous spend buy American beautiful

Interviewer: How old are you, Mr Adams?

Henry Adams: I'm .... years old.

Interviewer: How long have you been in London?

Henry Adams: Oh, I've been here about five ....

Interviewer: Do you know that you're the most .... person in London, at the moment?

Henry Adams: Well, yes, I've noticed that .... look at me, and .... me around town.

Interviewer: People say that you're a .... millionaire. Are you?

Henry Adams: Yes, I think I am! I am able to buy .... I want by showing my million-pound note.

Interviewer: What have you .... recently?

Henry Adams: I've always wanted a fast ...., and yesterday I found a .... black horse that I liked. I examined him carefully. I .... him for a few kilometres in the .... He was very fast and jumped fences well. So, I decided to .... him.

Interviewer: How much did you ....?

Henry Adams: Ah, that's a secret!

Interviewer: You're an ...., Mr Adams. What do you like best about the ....?

Henry Adams: I love their sense of ...., and I love their beautiful girls!

THE ORIGINS OF BANKING

Banking first appeared in Babylon in the year 1,000 BC. in the form of safekeeping; [1] lending and transfers. Banking also developed in Greece in the year 700 BC., and in Egypt in the year 400 BC.

Modern banking, as we know it today, began with Italian merchants and London goldsmiths, [2] who gave credit to depositors.

Between the 12th and the 15th centuries, Italy was Europe's most important financial and commercial power. In the 12th century, the banks of Genoa accepted deposits and exchanged foreign coins for local currency. Later, the Florentines became the leading Italian bankers.

The Medici Family of Florence was the greatest of all 15th century Italian bankers. They had offices in France, England, the Netherlands and throughout Italy. As time went on, banks developed all over Europe and in the New World.

1. **safekeeping** : protecting money or objects of value.
2. **goldsmiths** : people who make things out of gold.

Choose the correct answer.

a. Banking first appeared in:

☐ Italy
☐ Babylon
☐ Greece

b. Banking as we know it today began with:

☐ Egyptian merchants
☐ Greek merchants
☐ Italian merchants and London goldsmiths

c. Europe's most important financial and commercial power between the 12th and 15th centuries was:

☐ Italy
☐ England
☐ Florence

d. In the 12th century, the banks of Genoa:

☐ were very small
☐ had offices throughout Italy .
☐ accepted deposits and exchanged foreign coins

e. In the 15th century, the greatest Italian bankers were:

☐ the Medici Family of Florence
☐ the families of Genoa
☐ the goldsmiths of Florence

THE BANK OF ENGLAND

The Bank of England, England's central banking institution was founded in 1694, in Threadneedle Street in London's City. The Bank of England was formed because a central bank was needed to strengthen the

country's banking system.

As the Industrial Revolution grew, there was a real need for a more complex banking system. In Britain, the smaller "country" banks were gradually replaced by "joint-stock" banks [1] after 1826. The Bank Charter Act of 1844 confirmed the

role of the Bank of England as the central note-issuing authority of the English banking system.

By 1870, Britain was not only the centre of the world's industry and trade, but also the financial centre.

---

1. **"joint-stock" banks** : banks owned by all the people who have bought shares in them.

Are these sentences true (T) or false (F)? correct the false ones.

		T	F
1.	The Bank of England was founded in 1649 in Threadneedle Street in London's City.	☐	☐
2.	The Bank of England was formed because a central bank was needed to strengthen the country's banking system.	☐	☐
3.	With the Industrial Revolution there was a need for a simpler banking system.	☐	☐
4.	After 1826, "joint-stock" banks were replaced by "country banks".	☐	☐
5.	The Bank Charter Act of 1844 confirmed the role of the Bank of England as the central note issuing authority.	☐	☐
6.	By 1870, Britain was the financial centre of the world.	☐	☐

....
....
....
....

The film *Trading Places*, with Eddie Murphy, which was entitled 'Una Poltrona per Due' in Italian was based on the story you have just read.

Million-Pound Grammar

1 **Look at this sentence from Chapter One:**

'That night, when I *had lost* all hope, a small English brig saw me and took me on board.'
(*first*, the narrator loses all hope, *then* a brig sees him)
'had lost' is an example of the Past Perfect tense.

We use the Past Perfect to talk about a situation that happened before a particular time in the past.

He ate a big dinner.   Then he fell asleep.

After he had eaten a big dinner, he fell asleep.

Make one sentence using the Past Perfect and Past Simple with the help of the suggested adverb.

a. He had no money. He spent it all at Harris's Eating Place. (After)

b. He found the big banknote. Then he gave it to the Police. (As soon as)

c. Our friends left. Then we arrived at the park. (When)

Now complete these sentences by putting one verb into the Past Simple and the other into the Past Perfect:

d. We .... (walk) ten kilometres when we .... (decide) to stop and rest.

e. Lloyd .... (study) for a week when he finally .... (take) the test.

f. They .... (get) wet because they .... (forget) their umbrella.

Million-Pound Grammar

'If clauses'

2 **In Chapter Two, Brother A said to Brother B:**

'*If* an honest and intelligent stanger *arrives* in London without a friend and without money, except for the £1,000,000 banknote, he *will* starve to death.'

We use 'if clauses' (first conditional) to talk about a possible future situation and its results.

if + Present Simple + will

Look at this example:

If he (go) to the bank, the police (arrest) him.
If he goes to the bank, the police will arrest him.

Complete the following sentences:

a. If he .... (be) honest and intelligent, he .... (be) the right man for the bet.

b. If it .... (rain), we .... (not go) to the park.

c. If he .... (open) the envelope, ... he (find) a letter.

d. I .... (win) the bet, if I .... (follow) the instructions.

e. The wind .... (push) me out of the bay, if I .... (sail) out too far.

f. Their future .... (be) promising, if they .... (work) hard.

Million-Pound Grammar

3 **In Chapter Three, we see this sentence:**

'I *must* keep the bill for a whole month. And, I *must* not lose it.'

We use 'must' and 'mustn't' to talk about obligation and necessity, in the present and future.

Look at these pictures and make a sentence describing the message of the picture, using *must* or *mustn't*.

a. ....

b. ....

c. ....

d. ....

e. ....

f. ....

g. ....

Million-Pound Grammar

4 **Look at this sentence from Chapter Four:**

The blue suit was *worse* than the brown one. (***worse* is a comparative**)
He chose the *worst* for me. (***worst* is a superlative**)

Some forms are irregular:

ADJECTIVE	COMPARATIVE	SUPERLATIVE
good	better	best
bad	worse	worst

With one-syllable adjectives, we add -er for the comparative form, and -est for the superlative form.

ADJECTIVE	COMPARATIVE	SUPERLATIVE
cold	colder	coldest
young	younger	youngest

Fill in the gaps with the correct form of either the comparative or superlative:

a.   Tod was .... (poor) than the shop owner. The narrator was the .... person in the shop.

b.   The west wind was cold, but the east wind was .... The north wind was the ....

c.   This cloak is .... (simple) than the coat. But the mantel is the .... of all.

d.   Brother A was .... (happy) than Brother B, but the narrator was the ....

e.   The shop owner was................. (kind) than Tod. Harris was the .... of all.

f.   The servant had a big lunch. Brother A had a .... lunch than Brother B. But the narrator had the .... lunch of all.

Million-Pound Grammar

5 Let's fill in the verb table. One is done for you.

INFINITIVE	PAST SIMPLE	PAST PARTICIPLE	REGULAR or IRREGULAR
buy	bought	bought	irregular
	was/were		
		preferred	
become			
	drew		
		done	
keep			
	wore		
		known	
think			
	planned		
		sold	
win			
		paid	
say			

Million-Pound Grammar

6 **In Chapter Six we see these sentences:**

'I remember *clearly.*'
'Mr Adams,' she said *softly* and smiled, 'I love you too!'

Clearly and *softly* are adverbs.
Adverbs describe verbs, other adverbs or adjectives.
Adverbs answer questions such as: how? when? where?

Look at these examples:
He spoke calmly. (*calmly* **describes how he spoke.**)
She went to a party yesterday. (*yesterday* **describes when she went to the party.**)
They sat there. (*there* **describes where they sat.**)

Fill in the gaps with the correct adverb from the box:

tomorrow	here	suddenly	slowly and carefully
	today	quickly	well

a. He will pay for the suit ....

b. ...., he became famous.

c. Henry Adams met the Ambassador ....

d. 'Please sit ....,' said Lloyd.

e. We ran across the street ....

f. Henry read the letter ....

g. We didn't feel .... after the dinner.